GARFIELD Classics
Volume Seven

MY SEVENTH CLASSIC COLLECTION
CONTAINS:

GOING PLACES

LE MAGNIFIQUE!

IN THE FAST LANE

JiM DAViS

First published by Ravette Publishing 2001
Reprinted 2003

Printed and bound in Great Britain
for Ravette Publishing Limited,
Unit 3, Tristar Centre,
Star Road, Partridge Green,
West Sussex RH13 8RA
by Cox & Wyman Ltd, Reading, Berkshire

ISBN: 1 84161 088 7

Garfield

Going Places

JIM DAVIS

JiM DAV959-4

IN CASE YOU'RE INTERESTED, WATCHES DON'T FLOAT

YOU MIGHT BE INTERESTED TO KNOW WHILE *YOU* WERE ASLEEP, I CAUGHT A MOUSE

© 1988 United Feature Syndicate, Inc.

GOOD BOY

JIM DAVIS

9-29

WHIP

A LITTLE SENSITIVE ABOUT OUR WEIGHT, ARE WE?

MY WEIGHT, MY BUSINESS

JIM DAVIS

10-11

© 1988 United Feature Syndicate, Inc.

© 1988 United Feature Syndicate, Inc.

RATS. I HATE STATIC ELECTRICITY

JIM DAVIS 10-18

SO DO I

10-24

JiM DAViS   10-26

© 1988 United Feature Syndicate, Inc.

© 1988 United Feature Syndicate, Inc.

© 1988 United Feature Syndicate, Inc.

DARN THING'S DEFECTIVE

JIM DAVIS

12-23

© 1988 United Feature Syndicate, Inc.

THIS YEAR, I RESOLVE TO BE GENTLER WITH ODIE!

PUSH

JIM DAVIS 12-30

Garfield
Le Magnifique!

JIM DAVIS

2-2

BWOING!

BREAKFAST IN BED, GARFIELD?

SLOTH IS THE MOTHER OF INVENTION

JRM DAVPS

DOGS ARE THE ANIMAL BY-PRODUCTS IN THE WEENIE OF LIFE

DEPRESSED, GARFIELD?

HOW COULD YOU TELL?

JIM DAVIS

WHIRR

© 1989 United Feature Syndicate, Inc.

2-14

JIM DAVIS

JIM DAVIS 2-15

© 1989 United Feature Syndicate, Inc.

WHAT DO YOU GET WHEN YOU CROSS
A DOG WITH A NINE-FOOT GORILLA?

YOU GET A GORILLA THAT DRINKS
OUT OF ANY TOILET HE PLEASES!

© 1989 United Feature Syndicate, Inc.

JIM DAVIS 3-9

POIT

© 1989 United Feature Syndicate, Inc.

JiM DAViS 3-13

SNIP!

AIEEEEE

3-14

JPM DAVIS

JIM DAVIS

3-16

SQUISH

JIM DAVIS   3-17

"WHAP!"

© 1989 United Feature Syndicate, Inc.

JIM DAVIS 3-18

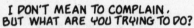

JIM DAVIS

3-27

PSHHHHH

4-5

JiM DAViS

© 1989 United Feature Syndicate, Inc.

SCRIBBLE
SCRIBBLE
SCRIBBLE

JIM DAVIS

4-8

4-13

JiM DAViS

GOOD, GARFIELD'S NOT AROUND.
I WON'T HAVE TO SHARE MY MILK

© 1989 United Feature Syndicate, Inc.

JIM DAVIS

4-20

POOR ODIE. LOCKED OUTSIDE IN THE COLD. I JUST CAN'T BEAR TO SEE HIM LIKE THIS. I GOTTA DO SOMETHING

SHOONK

4-26

TAP
TAP!

© 1989 United Feature Syndicate, Inc.

JIM DAVIS

JIM DAVIS   5-27

© 1989 United Feature Syndicate, Inc.

JIM DAVIS   6-3

JIM DAVIS

6-8

Garfield
'n The Fast Lane

JiM DAViS

© 1989 United Feature Syndicate, Inc.

© 1989 United Feature Syndicate, Inc.

JIM DAVIS 7-1

© 1989 United Feature Syndicate, Inc.

LUNCH, GARFIELD!

DON'T TOUCH HIM OR YOU'LL LOSE MY PAGE

7-20

JPM DAVPS

7-22

© 1989 United Feature Syndicate, Inc.

© 1989 United Feature Syndicate, Inc.

7-29

© 1989 United Feature Syndicate, Inc.

JIM DAVIS 8-1

© 1989 United Feature Syndicate, Inc.

JIM DAVIS

8-3

WHAT THE...?

© 1989 United Feature Syndicate, Inc.

PENTHOUSE

8-7

JIM DAVIS

SCREEEEEEEEE

THONK

JIM DAVIS 8-16

© 1989 United Feature Syndicate, Inc.

© 1989 United Feature Syndicate, inc.

9-4   JPM DAVIS

© 1989 United Feature Syndicate, Inc.

© 1989 United Feature Syndicate, Inc.

© 1989 United Feature Syndicate, Inc.

9-18   JIM DAVIS

9-20

© 1989 United Feature Syndicate, Inc.

JIM DAVIS   9-29

JUST RIGHT!

© 1989 United Feature Syndicate, Inc.

JIM DAVIS

10-12

VERY FUNNY, GARFIELD! YOU CAN'T MAKE ME THINK YOUR TEDDY BEAR CAN SKATE!

© 1989 United Feature Syndicate, Inc.

SAY AGAIN?

JPM DAVPS

10-14

© 1989 United Feature Syndicate, Inc.

AFTER YEARS OF TAKING LIFE FOR GRANTED, GARFIELD IS SHAKEN BY A HORRIFYING VISION OF THE INEVITABLE PROCESS CALLED "TIME"

HE HAS ONLY ONE WEAPON...

DENIAL...

I DON'T WANT TO BE ALONE

WANT SOME BREAKFAST, GARFIELD?

WHO NEEDS IT? I NEED YOU!

AN IMAGINATION IS A POWERFUL TOOL. IT CAN TINT MEMORIES OF THE PAST, SHADE PERCEPTIONS OF THE PRESENT, OR PAINT A FUTURE SO VIVID THAT IT CAN ENTICE... OR TERRIFY, ALL DEPENDING UPON HOW WE CONDUCT OURSELVES TODAY...

END

© 1989 United Feature Syndicate, Inc.

OTHER GARFIELD BOOKS AVAILABLE

Pocket Books	Price	ISBN
Bon Appetit	£3.50	1 84161 038 0
Byte Me	£3.50	1 84161 009 7
Double Trouble	£3.50	1 84161 008 9
Eat My Dust	£3.50	1 84161 098 4
Fun in the Sun	£3.50	1 84161 097 6
The Gladiator	£3.50	1 85304 941 7
Gooooooal!	£3.50	1 84161 037 2
Great Impressions	£3.50	1 85304 191 2
In Training	£3.50	1 85304 785 6
The Irresistible	£3.50	1 85304 940 9
Let's Party	£3.50	1 85304 906 9
Light Of My Life	£3.50	1 85304 353 2
On The Right Track	£3.50	1 85304 907 7
Pick Of The Bunch	£2.99	1 85304 258 7
Says It With Flowers	£2.99	1 85304 316 8
Shove At First Sight	£3.50	1 85304 990 5
To Eat, Or Not To Eat?	£3.50	1 85304 991 3
Wave Rebel	£3.50	1 85304 317 6
With Love From Me To You	£3.50	1 85304 392 3

new titles now available		
No. 45 – Pop Star	£3.50	1 84161 151 4
No. 46 – Below Par	£3.50	1 84161 152 2

Theme Books	Price	ISBN
Guide to Behaving Badly	£4.50	1 85304 892 5
Guide to Cat Napping	£4.50	1 84161 087 9
Guide to Coffee Mornings	£4.50	1 84161 086 0
Guide to Creatures Great & Small	£3.99	1 85304 998 0
Guide to Healthy Living	£3.99	1 85304 972 7
Guide to Pigging Out	£4.50	1 85304 893 3
Guide to Romance	£3.99	1 85304 894 1
Guide to The Seasons	£3.99	1 85304 999 9
Guide to Successful Living	£3.99	1 85304 973 5

2-in-1 Theme Books	Price	ISBN
The Gruesome Twosome	£6.99	1 84161 143 3
Out For The Couch	£6.99	1 84161 144 1

Classics	Price	ISBN
Volume One	£5.99	1 85304 970 0
Volume Two	£5.99	1 85304 971 9
Volume Three	£5.99	1 85304 996 4
Volume Four	£5.99	1 85304 997 2
Volume Five	£5.99	1 84161 022 4
Volume Six	£5.99	1 84161 023 2
Volume Eight	£5.99	1 84161 089 5
Volume Nine	£5.99	1 84161 149 2
Volume Ten	£5.99	1 84161 150 6

Little Books		
Food 'n' Fitness	£2.50	1 84161 145 X
Laughs	£2.50	1 84161 146 8
Love 'n' Stuff	£2.50	1 84161 147 6
Wit 'n' Wisdom	£2.50	1 84161 148 4

Miscellaneous

new title available June 2003

	Price	ISBN
25 Years of Me!	£7.99	1 84161 173 5
Treasury 3	£9.99	1 84161 142 5
Treasury 2	£9.99	1 84161 042 9
Address Book (indexed) inc vat	£4.99	1 85304 904 2
21st Birthday Celebration Book	£9.99	1 85304 995 6

All Garfield books are available at your local bookshop or from the publisher at the address below. Just tick the titles required and send the form with your payment to:-

RAVETTE PUBLISHING
Unit 3, Tristar Centre, Star Road, Partridge Green, West Sussex RH13 8RA

Prices and availability are subject to change without notice.
Please enclose a cheque or postal order made payable to **Ravette Publishing** to the value of the cover price of the book and allow the following for UK postage and packing:

60p for the first book + 30p for each additional book
except *Garfield Treasuries* and *21st Birthday Celebration Book* . . . when please add £3.00 per copy for p&p

Name ....

Address ....

....

....